What can I be?

3

Too scary.

Too hairy.

7

Too silly.

Too frilly.

Too green.

Too mean!

Too hot.

17

Too many spots!

What can I be?

I can be me!

Word List (15 words)

be	hot	scary
can	I	silly
frilly	many	spots
green	me	too
hairy	mean	what

About the Author

Cari Meister lives on a small farm in Minnesota with her husband John, her sons Edwin, Benjamin, and Aaron, their dog Samson, two horses, three cats, two pigs, and two goats. She is the author of more than twenty books for children, including *I Love Rocks*, *Game Day*, and *A New Roof* in the *A Rookie Reader* series.

About the Illustrator

Matt Phillips has been doodling since he could hold his dad's fountain pen without poking himself. He's been happily drawing ever since. Sometimes he stops to play the mandolin or banjo or squeak away on the fiddle, but he pretty much draws all the time. He has a wonderful wife who teaches school, and two dogs that don't teach anything. He also has a cat that likes to knock over his ink and ruin final art with her inky footprints. His doodles can be found in books, magazines, malls, greeting cards, websites, advertisements, and little wadded up piles all around his drawing table. He lives and works in White, Georgia.

My Grandpa often shows me
his family photos. He's proud of his children
and his grandchildren. Especially me.

a gift for us to share

to: ...A. Hunter......

from:
....

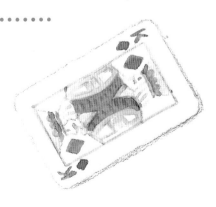

OTHER HELEN EXLEY GIFTBOOKS IN THIS SERIES:

Me and my Mum

Me and my Mom

Me and my Dad

Me and my Friend

Me and my Grandma

Me and my Teacher

OTHER HELEN EXLEY GIFTBOOKS:

Giggles: A Joke Book

Crazy Kids' Jokes

To a very special Grandpa

Published in 2006 by Helen Exley Giftbooks in Great Britain,
and Helen Exley Giftbooks LLC in the USA.

12   11   10   9   8   7   6   5   4   3   2

Illustrations © Jane Massey 2006
Copyright © Helen Exley 2006
The moral right of the author has been asserted.

ISBN 978-1-90513-085-6

A copy of the CIP data is available from the British Library on request.

Printed in China

Helen Exley Giftbooks, 16 Chalk Hill, Watford, Herts WD19 4BG, UK,
www.helenexleygiftbooks.com

Me and my Grandpa

Written by Helen Exley and Illustrated by Jane Massey

I love my Grandpa.

And I love it most when I stay with him.

He always waits by the window

for me to arrive.

When I stay at Grandpa's
he always has a special look
in his eye, and a kind of soft smile.
I help him build things in his workshop.
We eat chocolate bars that
he buys specially for me.
Usually he forgets they're for me
and eats most of them himself.

Grandpa marks pages in his books to read with me. Did you know that he keeps hundreds and hundreds of his old books just to share with me?

Grandpa tells me that he used to do rough and tumble things with my Dad. But now it seems they're both past it. Grandpa's still quite strong, though. When he took me golfing, one shot broke the clubhouse window.

Grandpa's good fun, and he's game for almost anything. But he turns a bit green on round-a-bouts and swings, so then I have to look after him.

I write to my Grandpa and tell him
all the news. He writes back to me.
It used to be to help me to learn to read
but now it stops us both from being lonely.

My Grandpa always, always carries my letters in his briefcase when he goes to work.
He reads them and looks at all the photos of our family. And of me.

Grandpa and I
just play and play, and talk and talk.
But then Grandpa gets tired
and goes to sleep.
Then it's my turn to watch out for him,
so I have to keep very QUIET.

Do you know that every year
Grandpa grows strawberries just for me?
How can I ever say "Thank you"
for the strawberries and the chocolates
and the hugs and letters?

There are no words that
can ever say "Thank you" big enough!

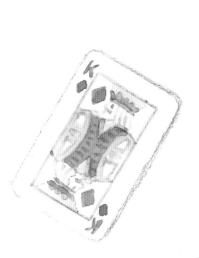

WHAT IS A HELEN EXLEY GIFTBOOK?

Helen Exley Giftbooks cover the most powerful of all human relationships:
the bonds within families and between friends, and the theme of personal values.
No expense is spared in making sure that each book is as meaningful
a gift as it is possible to create: good to give, good to receive.
You have the result in your hands. If you have loved it – tell others!
There is no power on earth like the word-of-mouth recommendation of friends!